Contents

Written by
David Grant

Illustrated by
Paul Williams

Series editor **Dee**

PEARSON

D0434433

Before reading Fame Over

New vocabulary

ch1 p4 practising
ch1 p4 producer
ch1 p6 squealed

ch1 p7 tone deaf
ch3 p13 excuse
ch4 p17 own up

Introduction

Nothing exciting ever happens to Joe and Tom, so Joe decides to pretend that they have started a band and are about to go on tour with the cool band, 'No Way'. Joe's lies create a lot of problems for Tom.

Fame Over

Chapter One

"I'm so bored," said Joe.

"Me too," said Tom. "Nothing exciting ever happens to us."

Just then Becky came over. "What's new, you losers?" she said.

"We're not losers," said Joe. "You know what, something really exciting has happened."

"Yeah? What?" said Becky.

"We're going to be pop stars," said Joe suddenly. "Tom and I started a band a few months ago."

"Did we?" said Tom with a surprised look on his face.

"Yeah," said Joe. "We've been practising non-stop and we've been discovered by a famous music producer."

Joe's phone rang. "Hello?" he said. "Yeah? That's great news. See you then."

"That was our manager," explained Joe. "We're going into the recording studio at the weekend to record our first CD."

"Fantastic!" screamed Becky.

"That's not all," said Joe. "We're also going on tour with 'No Way'."

"'No Way'?" said Becky. "Are you serious? They're my most favourite band in the world!"

"We're meeting them this weekend," said Joe.

"That is so cool!" squealed Becky and she ran off to tell her friends.

"Why did you say all that?" said Tom. "It's not true. We can't even sing. We're both tone deaf."

Joe grinned. "I was bored," he said.

Chapter Two

That lunchtime, Joe and Tom were chatting in the canteen. Becky came up to them with all her friends.

"Hi guys," she said.

Joe's mobile buzzed. "Hello?" said Joe. "Hi Ben, how's it going?"

"It's Ben from 'No Way'," whispered Joe. He moved away, talking on his phone.

Becky's mouth fell open. "Can you get me a signed photo of Ben from 'No Way'?" she begged.

"Maybe," said Tom.

Joe came back. He smiled at Tom. "They're picking us up at eleven on Saturday morning to take us to the recording studio," he said.

Then Becky's friend Meg spoke to Tom. "Do you fancy going to the cinema tonight?" she said.

Tom couldn't believe his ears. He had fancied Meg for ages. "Yeah, OK," he said. He knew she had only asked him because she thought he might become famous.

Tom decided he should tell her the truth. "Meg, I need to tell you something."

"What?" asked Meg and she gave him a big smile.

"Nothing," said Tom. "It doesn't matter."

Chapter Three

After school finished, Joe came running up to Tom. "Guess what!" he said.

"What?" said Tom.

"I just saw Mr Blunt," said Joe. Mr Blunt was their Head of Year. "He's heard about the band and he wants us to sing in assembly."

"What!" said Tom. "What excuse did you give him?"

"I couldn't think of an excuse," said Joe, "so I said yes."

"You did what?" screamed Tom. "When does he want us to sing?"

"Tomorrow," said Joe.

"I'm going to kill you," said Tom. "We're going to look stupid in front of the whole school."

"Don't worry," said Joe. "I'll think of something."

That night, Tom and Meg went to the cinema but Tom didn't really enjoy the film. He was too worried about singing in assembly the next day.

"What's the matter?" asked Meg. "You're not nervous about tomorrow are you?"

"Me?" said Tom. "Course not."

Chapter Four

The next morning, Tom went to the assembly hall. There were two microphones on the stage. But there was no sign of Joe.

"Are you all ready for your big performance?" said Mr Blunt. Tom tried to smile. He felt sick.

The hall was starting to fill up. But there was still no sign of Joe. Tom sent him a text. Joe sent a text back saying:

got a sore throat sorry. won't be coming into school.

Tom decided to own up to Mr Blunt. But Mr Blunt was already talking to the assembly. "We have a special performance today," said Mr Blunt. "Tom and Joe are going to sing for us."

Everyone clapped. Tom stepped on to the stage. He stood by one of the microphones.

Tom looked at the audience. The audience looked at him. "I've got some bad news," said Tom. "Joe and I have agreed to split up. We're so upset about it we've decided we're never going to sing again. Sorry."

Tom hurried off the stage. Some boys in the audience booed. Becky looked upset.

After the assembly Tom was still worried. He thought Meg only liked him because she thought he was going to be famous. Now he had to tell her the truth. Meg came running up to Tom. She gave him a big hug.

"I can't believe you're never going to sing again," she said. "You must be gutted."

"There's something I need to tell you," said Tom.

"You can't really sing, can you?" said Meg.

"No," said Tom.

Meg smiled. "Shall we go into town after school and buy some chips?" she asked.

"Excellent!" said Tom. He grinned back.

Quiz

Text comprehension

Literal comprehension
p7 Why is it a bad idea that Joe pretends they are in a band?

p14 Why did Tom not really enjoy the film?

p18 How does Tom get out of singing in assembly?

Inferential comprehension
p16 Do you think Joe really has a sore throat?

p18 Why is Tom's excuse a good one?

p19 Do you think Meg suspects Tom earlier? Why?

Personal response
- How would you feel if you had to sing in front of the school assembly?
- Do you think Joe will have learned his lesson about telling lies?
- Do you think Tom and Joe will still be friends?

Author's style

p13 Why is 'screamed' a good speech verb to use here?

p15 Why does the author make Mr Blunt call it a 'big performance'?

p18 Why does the author use two very similar sentences at the top of the page?

Characters

- **Tom's mum**
- **Arif** (a school friend)
- **Tom**
- Joe

Setting the scene

Joe told everyone at school that he and Tom have started a band. Their Head of Year has asked them to sing in the school assembly the next day. The problem is, Joe and Tom are both tone deaf! They're round at Tom's house rehearsing when Tom's mum rushes in.

Mum: What on earth is that terrible noise?

Arif: Tom and Joe are singing.

Mum: I didn't hear anyone singing. It sounded like someone hurting a cat.

Tom: *(to Joe)* I told you we were no good.

Mum: What's going on, you two?

Joe: I told everyone that Tom and I are in a band and we're going to be famous. Now we have to sing to everyone in assembly tomorrow.

Tom: And we sound like two cats being run over by a car.

Joe: I think we just need a bit more practice.

Arif: You two could practise for the next three years and you'd still sound terrible.

Joe: I thought we sounded pretty good.

Tom: What are you saying? We stink. We're terrible. We're tone deaf.

Arif: Yeah, give up, Joe.

Tom: We're the worst singers in the world. In the universe. We're the worst singers in the history of the universe, and tomorrow we're going to get laughed out of school.

Mum: They might not laugh.

Arif: Oh yes they will! But it gets worse.

Tom: Much worse.

Mum: What are you on about?

Arif: Tom was asked out by the girl of his dreams. They are going to the cinema.

Tom: Yeah, in about five minutes.

Mum: So what's the problem?

Arif: When Meg hears him singing tomorrow, she's going to laugh in his face.

Mum: And you think she'll never want to see you again?

Joe: Did you say Meg will be round in five minutes? We'd better have one more practice.

Arif: Do you have to?

Joe: Ready, Tom? One,
two, three, four...

Tom and Joe: *(singing very badly)* I love you,
yes I do, my love is true...

Mum: Stop, stop, stop!

Joe: What's the problem?

Mum: Shouldn't you both be singing the
same tune?

Joe: We *are* singing the same tune.

Tom: I don't think we're singing *any* tune.

Joe: I thought we sounded pretty good. What did you two think?

Arif: It was the worst thing I ever heard.

Mum: I've heard worse. Tom shut his hand in the car door about two years ago. You should have heard him scream. *That* was the worst thing I ever heard!

Arif: But his singing is the second worst thing you ever heard?

Mum: Yeah.

The doorbell rings.

Tom: Oh no, that's Meg! How do I look?

Arif: Better than you sound.

Quiz

Text comprehension

p24 How can you tell Arif thinks Tom and Joe are hopeless at singing?

p25 How does Mum try to cheer them up?

p27 How can you tell Mum thinks Tom and Joe are hopeless at singing?

Vocabulary

p22 Find a word meaning 'awful'.

p23 Find a word meaning 'very well known'.

p28 Find a word meaning 'most dreadful'.

Before reading SUPER FANS

Find out about

- the strange things some fans will buy.

New vocabulary

p33 idols
p33 owned
p35 museum

p35 guarded
p38 breathed

Introduction

Lots of people like to buy things to show they are a fan of something. People buy football shirts or magazines. But some fans pay lots of money for some very strange things.

SUPER FANS

Are you a fan of something? Have you ever bought something to show you are a fan? Maybe you've bought a football shirt or a magazine about your favourite singer. But some fans pay lots of money for some very strange things.

Two of the best-selling artists of all time were Elvis Presley and Michael Jackson. Between them they sold nearly 2 billion records.

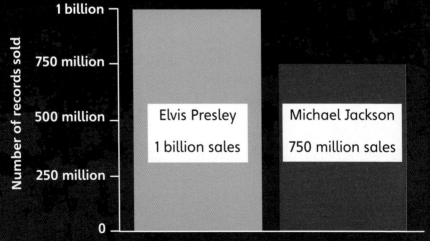

Number of records sold

1 billion

750 million

500 million

250 million

0

Elvis Presley
1 billion sales

Michael Jackson
750 million sales

Best-selling artists

Some fans are so keen to have something their idols once owned, they have bought some crazy things that are very expensive.

Elvis Presley

Elvis died in 1977. Since then, some Elvis fans have paid lots of money to get hold of some of the things he once owned. One fan bought a medicine bottle which Elvis had once used. The fan paid £1,600 for the medicine bottle. Another fan bought a microphone which Elvis had once used. The fan bought the microphone for £9,000.

A teddy bear that Elvis once owned was lent to a museum. There were lots of teddy bears in the museum. The museum was guarded at night by a dog called Barney. One night Barney went crazy and attacked the teddy bears, ripping them to pieces. One of the bears he attacked was Elvis's teddy bear. It was worth £40,000.

Michael Jackson

Some Michael Jackson fans have paid lots of money to get hold of something the singer once owned. The jacket he wore in the video of his record 'Thriller' sold for £1.1 million. The glittery glove which he wore when he first did his moonwalk dance in 1983 was sold for £220,000.

In 1984, when Michael was making an advert for Pepsi, a firework exploded and his hair caught fire. Twenty-five years later, a fan bought twelve of Michael's burnt hairs for over £1,000!

Michael's 'Thriller' jacket

Super Strange

Some very strange things have been sold on internet websites. A fan paid a lot of money for a piece of gum chewed by Britney Spears and one fan bought a piece of toast that Justin Timberlake had half eaten.

One girl even tried to sell a bottle of air breathed out by the singer Pink. She had been to a Pink concert and said she had caught some of Pink's breath in a bottle. But it sold for less than a pound. So some things are so crazy that even a super fan won't pay for them!

Quiz

Text comprehension

Literal comprehension

p32 Why are Elvis Presley and Michael Jackson described as 'best-selling' artists?

p35 Why was Barney not such a good guard dog?

p36 How much did one fan pay for Michael Jackson's jacket?

Inferential comprehension

p33 Why are some things fans have bought described as 'crazy'?

p34 Why might people pay more for things after their idol has died?

p38 Why do you think fans wouldn't pay much for the bottle of Pink's breath?

Personal response

- Are you a fan of something?
- How do you think the museum staff felt when Barney destroyed Elvis's teddy bear?
- What do you think makes some fans spend so much money on strange things?

Non-fiction features

p34–35 Think of labels for the pictures on these pages.

p36 Think of a subheading for the text below the picture.

p38 Why is there an exclamation mark at the end of the final sentence?

Published by Pearson Education Limited, Edinburgh Gate, Harlow, Essex, CM20 2JE.

www.pearsonschoolsandfecolleges.co.uk

Text © Pearson Education Limited 2012

Edited by Jo Dilloway
Designed by Tony Richardson and Siu Hang Wong
Original illustrations © Pearson Education Limited 2012
Illustrated by Paul Williams
Cover design by Siu Hang Wong
Picture research by Melissa Allison
Cover illustration © Pearson Education Limited 2012

The right of David Grant to be identified as author of this work has been asserted by him in accordance with the Copyright, Designs and Patents Act 1988.

First published 2012

16 15 14 13 12
10 9 8 7 6 5 4 3 2 1

British Library Cataloguing in Publication Data
A catalogue record for this book is available from the British Library

ISBN 978 0 435 07150 9

Printed at Scotprint, UK.

Acknowledgements
The author and publisher would like to thank the following individuals and organisations for permission to reproduce photographs:

(Key: b-bottom; c-centre; l-left; r-right; t-top)

Alamy Images: Photos 12 37t; Getty Images: Getty Images Entertainment / Samir Hussein 36, TIME & LIFE Images / Charles Trainor 1, 32; iStockphoto: cynoclub 35; Press Association Images: All Action / EMPICS Entertainment 33, Empics Entertainment / Mehdi Taamallah / ABACA USA 38r; Shutterstock.com: Dziurek 31, R. Gino Santa Maria 34, Szymon Apanowicz 38l, Tihis 37b

Cover images: Back: Press Association Images: Empics Entertainment / Mehdi Taamallah / ABACA USA

All other images © Pearson Education

Every effort has been made to contact copyright holders of material reproduced in this book. Any omissions will be rectified in subsequent printings if notice is given to the publishers.